We love Alex and Hannah. So much  about walking with God and expe love this series.

Dr. Kwesi Kamau, Lead Pastor, IMPACT Church, Dallas TX

The Naturally Supernatural Course helped me live with a different awareness of God's supernatural activity and equipped me with practical tools that help me live more open to the supernatural work God wants to do in and through me. Alex and Hannah are great teachers (and fun)!

Tammy Melchien, Teaching Team Pastor, Community Christian Church, Chicago IL

The question that has dominated my thinking this last year is, 'What would it look like to let Jesus lead Jesus' church?' A large part of that answer has to be that Jesus' leaders need to know his voice. Alex and Hannah's approach to topics such as Hearing the Voice of God has been for me tremendously helpful, biblical and out right exciting. I could not commend them more strongly.

Chuck Gschwend, Founder of Renewal Coaching, AR

The Naturally Supernatural Course encouraged, challenged, and fed me spiritually, and God has used these times to deepen my relationship with the Holy Spirit. My view of God and my desire for Him has been enlarged through Alex and Hannah's leadership, and I have been equipped to lead our church through multiple series on the Spirit and His gifts.

Marshall Benbow, Lead Pastor, Grace Community Church, Greensboro NC

The Naturally Supernatural materials have been a great help in our personal discipleship and as we lead others. We have found ourselves being more attentive to the Holy Spirit's voice, more bold in asking for healing prayers and miracles. And God has been so faithful to answer!! These materials helped jump start us into a new season of being 'the Church' and participating in bringing God's kingdom where we live, work and play.

Steve and Cindy Shogren, Wellspring Ministries, Mount Pleasant UT

"I want to know Christ and the power of his resurrection and the sharing of his sufferings by becoming like him in his death" (Philippians 3:10). When meditating on this verse, I realized that I understood suffering but that I hadn't experienced much resurrection power in my spiritual life. God led me to the Absaloms' course, and coming from a church background that did not emphasize living supernaturally, I can say that I was not 'weirded out'! It really is natural. I took what I learned back to my church and we started developing the gift of prophecy (and we received words from God), prayer for healing (and we saw people healed), deliverance (and we saw people delivered), etc. This course helped to strengthen myself and my church in an area of weakness.

Jayme Himmelwright, Columbia SC

The Naturally Supernatural training was a true catalyst for my spiritual life. I did everything that Alex and Hannah taught and for the first time in my life I saw people get healed, I've shared prophetic words (that were accurate), and I've seen people freed from spiritual oppression. I highly recommend it.

Josh Wagner. Pastor. Indianapolis IN

I endorse this teaching with my whole heart. Gleaning from the expertise and experience that Alex and Hannah offer has greatly enhanced my ministry to others.

Bonnie C. Wetzel, MSW, LCSW, Raleigh NC

Alex and Hannah are a great team together. As someone who appreciates practical learning and application, we thoroughly enjoyed learning more about spiritual gifts taught in a very practical way. They gave us homework assignments to practically practice what we learned.

Jeremy and Andrea Harper, church planters, Columbus OH

Naturally Supernatural has been an incredible tool to come across. Straightforward, easy to understand, and biblically sound, the Absaloms have provided a resource that is imperative to our faith journey today. I highly recommend this course for churches and individuals alike.

Janine Koller, Prayer Director, Yakima WA

I've listened to God's voice for years, but the Naturally Supernatural Course has given me a biblical foundation that helps me understand and apply my prayer/prophetic experiences. I highly recommend this course to anyone who would like to grow in their ability to hear God's voice, or help others do so as well.

Emily Brown, Saugatuck MI

This course was incredibly helpful. All material was thoughtfully anchored in the Bible, and tremendously practical even for beginners looking to start ministering in the power of the Spirit. Alex and Hannah are humble, grounded, and eager to serve the church. Highly recommended!

John McHale, Mosaic Church of Richardson TX

The Naturally Supernatural Course helped me to start dialoguing with the Lord Jesus daily - not only praying, but asking Him and listening to Him. The Course changed my life!

Alena Vrlikova, Slovakia

The Naturally Supernatural Course has been wonderful for my growth in intimacy and partnership with the third person of the Trinity. It challenged my understanding of Scripture and has given me a great Kingdom framework to move out with the Spirit in proclaiming and demonstrating the power of the Gospel.

Lee Simmons, Pastor, Greensboro NC

The Naturally Supernatural Course was incredibly helpful! Alex and Hannah are thoughtful and encouraging guides that will help you hear the voice of God. Deeply theological and yet pragmatic and accessible! I wish I had found this course years ago!

Chris Brister, Lead Pastor, Union Church, Auburn AL

This material has truly been life changing for me - both personally and in ministry. It is full of biblical wisdom as well as practical steps to live a naturally supernatural life. I highly recommend this course!

Rachel Waldron, Destiny Church, Leesburg VA

THE

naturally

SUPERNATURAL

COURSE

COURSE BOOK A: FOUNDATIONS

Alex and Hannah Absalom

Dandelion Resourcing

The Naturally Supernatural Course - Course Book A: Foundations

Copyright © 2022 Alex and Hannah Absalom

Published by Dandelion Resourcing, Edmond, OK - dandelionresourcing.com

To contact Alex and Hannah about speaking at your conference or church, please visit dandelionresourcing.com

Design and Layout: Caity Shinnick

ISBN: 978-1-951420-04-8

With deepest gratitude to the many who have shown us — publicly and privately,
in person and in print — how to practice a naturally supernatural lifestyle.

CONTENTS

INTRODUCTION

Welcome to the Naturally Supernatural Course Book!

THE AIM OF THIS COURSE

The Naturally Supernatural Course is designed to help you discover how God has wired you to live a Spirit-empowered lifestyle.

As disciples of Jesus, we are given access to heavenly authority and power to play our part in extending His kingly rule. This is an empowering to build up the body of Christ in both depth and number.

However, so many believers don't know how to do this in practice. Whether it's a lack of healthy modeling, or few simple and repeatable practices, or the absence of clear Biblical undergirdings, or it simply slipping off our radar, the reality is that many of us struggle to healthily exercise a range of the naturally supernatural gifts of the Spirit.

This course is designed to help you:

- **UNCOVER** how to step more into the power and gifts of the Holy Spirit with the Naturally Supernatural Course.

- **BECOME** a biblically grounded practitioner of the more supernatural works of the Spirit.

- **EXPERIENCE** living by expectant faith while modeling pastoral kindness and love.

By God's grace, this is what lies in store for you now!

THE POWER OF COMMUNITY LEARNING

Most people will be watching these videos and doing the homework as part of a group of believers. While you can use this material by yourself - it will certainly still make sense and can be deeply applied - you will gain even more by buddying up with a few others from your church or ministry and working through it together. That way, you will learn from their stories and insights (as they will from you!), and there will be local accountability for following through on what you commit!

As you step into this resource, you'll see that there is plenty of space for you to write notes, add comments, ask questions, and discuss things with others in your local context. Remember that this is less about coming up with the 'right' set of answers, and more about allowing the Spirit to shape you through what you learn from the Bible, the teachings, your conversations, and your attempts to put things into practice in your everyday life.

OVERVIEW OF THE WHOLE COURSE

The whole course is divided into four parts, in order to give you bite sized chunks (the total 24 sessions could sound a bit intimidating!)

You have in your hands the Course Book for Part A: Foundations.

To help you see how this fits within the whole Naturally Supernatural Course, here's the Course overview:

PART A — FOUNDATIONS

MODULE A1: HEARING THE VOICE OF GOD
Session 1 - Prophecy Foundations
Session 2 - Prophecy Processing

MODULE A2: HEALING THE SICK
Session 1 - How to Minister Healing
Session 2 - Healing and Faith

MODULE A3: NATURALLY SUPERNATURAL THEOLOGY
Session 1 - The Naturally Supernatural Kingdom
Session 2 - Living in the Tension of the Now and the Not Yet

PART B — WARFARE

MODULE B1: BEING FILLED WITH THE HOLY SPIRIT
Session 1 - How to Be Filled With the Holy Spirit
Session 2 - The Gift of Tongues

MODULE B2: SPIRITUAL WARFARE
Session 1 - Biblical Ways to Understand the Battle
Session 2 - How to Develop Wise Warfare Strategies

MODULE B3: HOW TO DISCERN AND DRIVE OUT DEMONS
Session 1 - Biblical and Practical Foundations
Session 2 - Simple Steps to Minister Deliverance

PART C - EXPANSION

MODULE C1: WORDS OF KNOWLEDGE AND WORDS OF WISDOM
Session 1 - God's 'Now' Words of Life
Session 2 - How to Grow in Spiritual Hearing

MODULE C2: GROWING IN HEALING
Session 1 - Developing the Heart of a Healer
Session 2 - Emotional Healing

MODULE C3: THE GIFTS OF MIRACLES AND FAITH
Session 1 - Miracles and Everyday Life
Session 2 - Growing the Muscles of Faith

PART D - MULTIPLICATION

MODULE D1: NATURALLY SUPERNATURAL MISSION
Session 1 - The Naturally Supernatural Missionary
Session 2 - Spirit Empowered Evangelism

MODULE D2: RAISING NATURALLY SUPERNATURAL KIDS
Session 1 - Discipling the Next Generation
Session 2 - Helping All Kids Be Spirit Empowered

MODULE D3: DEVELOPING A PROPHETIC CULTURE
Session 1 - Growing Prayer Ministry
Session 2 - Prophecy in the Life of the Church

HOW TO USE THE MATERIAL

1. WHAT HAPPENS

Within each session you will receive teaching totaling around 40 minutes, broken up into chunks. At regular intervals you will be asked to pause the video to answer an application question, engage with a self-assessment, or sometimes even try an activation exercise.

Each session will end with homework being set, followed by a discussion time in your local group. You'll see that we provide lists of questions in your Course Book to help that along, although feel free to ignore those and come up with your own better conversation starters!

If you perhaps miss your session and are catching up later on, or if you are going through the Course by yourself, we suggest you write down your responses in this Course Book. That will help you frame your thoughts more clearly (as would happen in a conversation), and will build clearer action steps for you to live out.

Finally, if you haven't yet purchased access to the videos, or you haven't yet created your own account as part of your church's pass, then please go to naturallysupernaturalcourse.com.

2. HOMEWORK

As you have seen from the Course overview, each Module has two sessions within it. We've designed it this way because that creates time and space for you to ponder that topic over the following days, coming back to the second session with reflections and questions.

To help this process along, at the end of every session we give you homework!!

Don't freak out, though, if you don't think of yourself as particularly academic. The homework will always be practical. It is intended to help you live differently, so you'll find it's not about hitting the books or doing memorization, but rather immersing yourself into a new (or renewed) skill set.

Sometimes you will find the homework to be very stretching - which is on purpose! For instance, when you are in the module on healing the sick, one homework is to pray for at least four different people for healing between the sessions. While obviously there's nothing special about the number four, the point is that we want you to try ministering healing on multiple occasions, so that you gain a range of experiences. If we just said, 'try once', then everything would hang or fall on how well that one attempt went down!

Don't worry if you 'fail' or struggle with the homework. As long as you process and then grow, you will perhaps learn even more from those tough moments. Don't forget, the goal here is living out what you are discovering about the Spirit's empowering presence in and through you.

So please embrace the homework exercises. They're actually a lot of fun, and we're sure that as your group recounts their experiences, you will laugh, ponder, and be stretched in your own faith.

MODULE A1:

Hearing the Voice of God

SESSION 1:
PROPHECY FOUNDATIONS

INTRODUCTION

God is so relational and loves to communicate with us. Jesus died on the cross to bring us back into a relationship with God.

Prophecy, in its simplest form, is hearing from the Holy Spirit and sharing what He said.

> *"Would that all the Lord's people were prophets, that the Lord would put His Spirit upon them!"* (Numbers 11:29)

> *"I keep asking that the God of our Lord Jesus Christ, the glorious Father, may give you the Spirit of wisdom and revelation, so that you may know him better"* (Ephesians 1:17)

Jesus said,

> *"My sheep listen to my voice."* (John 10:27)

REFLECTION

Bring to mind a time when you felt God prompt you, you acted on it, and some-thing amazing (to a greater or lesser degree) happened?

For example, you thought of a friend, you texted to say you were praying for them today, and they told you that the timing was perfect because of something significant going on for them.

Use the space below to reflect.

DEFINITION

PROPHECY: "The supernatural ability to know and appropriately speak the mind of God on a given subject at a given time by the prompting and inspiration of the Holy Spirit."

> *"Follow the way of love and eagerly desire gifts of the Spirit, especially prophecy The one who prophesies speaks to people for their strengthening, encouraging and comfort." (1 Corinthians 14:1, 3)*

5 DEFINING CHARACTERISTICS

1. PROPHECY IS TO STRENGTHEN, ENCOURAGE AND COMFORT.

2. IT'S ALL ABOUT LOVE.

3. IN RELATION TO TIME, PROPHECY CAN BE:

    A. HINDSIGHT ABOUT WHAT WE ALREADY KNOW,

    B. INSIGHT INTO THE PRESENT, OR

    C. FORESIGHT INTO THE FUTURE.

4. PROPHECY IS CLOSELY TIED TO BEING A DISCIPLE.

    A DISCIPLE IS A LEARNER, OR APPRENTICE.

5. A PROPHETIC WORD GENERALLY HAS 3 PARTS: REVELATION,
    INTERPRETATION, APPLICATION.

SELF-ASSESSMENT

How regularly do you stop and listen to God? Give yourself a number between 1
and 5, with 1 being that you almost never do so, and 5 being that you frequently
pause to hear from Him.

Circle your answer.

| 1 | 2 | 3 | 4 | 5 |

What is it that most stops you from stopping to listen more?

Use the space below to reflect.

THE EXAMPLE OF JESUS

· *"The Son can do nothing by himself; he can do only what he sees his Father doing, because whatever the Father does the Son also does."* (John 5:19)

· The woman at the well (John 4:17-18)

· Predicting Peter's denial (Luke 22:34)

· 'Seeing' Nathaniel under the tree (John 1:47, 48)

· Foretelling the destruction of Jerusalem (Mark 13)

THE EXAMPLE OF THE EARLY CHURCH

· *"But the Helper, the Holy Spirit, whom the Father will send in my name, he will teach you all things and bring to your remembrance all that I have said to you."* (John 14:26)

· Peter at Pentecost (Acts 2, interpreting Joel 2)

· Peter knew that Ananias and Sapphira were lying (Acts 5:3)

· *"The Spirit told Philip, 'Go to that chariot and stay near it'."* (Acts 8:29)

· Agabus predicted a coming famine (Acts 11:28), and later Paul's imprisonment in Jerusalem (Acts 21:11

· *"Paul looked directly at [the lame man], saw that he had faith to be healed..."* (Acts 14:9)

REVELATION

"For God speaks in one way, and in two, though man does not perceive it." (Job 33:14)

1. BIBLE — "All scripture is God breathed..." (2 Timothy 3:16)

2. SEEING STUFF — *"He replied, 'I saw Satan fall like lightning from heaven.'"* (Luke 10:18)

3. HEARING STUFF — Elijah and the still small voice in 1 Kings 19.

4. GUT SENSE — *"Jesus knew in his spirit that this was what they were thinking."* (Mark 2:8)

5. FEELINGS — *"As he approached Jerusalem and saw the city, he wept over it."* (Luke 19:41)

6. BODIES — God's glory impacts the priests' ability to stand (1 Kings 8)

7. DREAMS — *"And having been warned in a dream not to go back to Herod, they returned to their country by another route."* (Matthew 2:12)

8. CREATION — *"The heavens declare the glory of God; the skies proclaim the work of his hands."* (Psalm 19:1)

9. PHYSICAL SEEING AND HEARING — *"One night the Lord spoke to Paul in a vision..."* (Acts 18:9

10. ANGELS — *"The angel went to her and said, 'Greetings, you who are highly favored! The Lord is with you.'"* (Luke 1:28)

11. CIRCUMSTANCES — *"Now when I went to Troas to preach the gospel of Christ and found that the Lord had opened a door for me."* (2 Corinthians 2:12)

12. ANYTHING! — What would you include?

ACTIVATION EXERCISE

Ask God to highlight something around you in the room. Ask Him what He wants to say to you through it.

TIPS:

Which object first grabs your attention? Why? Ask God if it symbolizes anything or what He might be saying through it.

Don't dismiss what first comes to mind ("That was probably just me...")

Use the space below to reflect.

HOW DO I KNOW IT'S GOD RATHER THAN THE DEVIL OR JUST ME?

1. LIFE

2. LEFT FIELD

3. LIGHTWEIGHT

4. DOUBT

5. '6TH SENSE'

6. REACTION

7. REPEATING

8. A GENERAL EXHORTATION

9. QUALITY

10. RISK

HOMEWORK

7 times in the next 2 weeks you are to prophesy over someone. Record the name, place, what happened, and the response you got.

TIPS:

Whenever you're praying for someone, don't solely pray but also ask God what He would like to say to them. (If you're not with them, text it to them).

If you need help, ask God to highlight something using a visual clue around you (similar to activation exercise), or from a Scripture, or simply close your eyes and pause in His presence as you lift that person before Him.

Record your experiences below.

1.

2.

3.

4.

5.

6.

7.

FURTHER DISCUSSION

We encourage you as a group to continue to process this content, along with other questions that you might have.

To help the conversation, here are a few stimulus questions:

1. What can you practically do to give Jesus room to speak?

2. With the prophecy you have experienced, would you say that it has mostly been hindsight, insight, or foresight oriented?

3. When have you or a family member experienced the love of God through prophecy?

4. What would you say is the main way that Jesus speaks to you? How many of the list of 12 have you experienced?

5. What helps you to assess whether a revelation is from God or not?

6. What excites you most about stepping further into the gift of prophecy?

MODULE A1:

Hearing the Voice of God

SESSION 2:
PROPHECY PROCESSING

HOMEWORK REVIEW

Did you prophesy over anyone? What happened?

What insights or questions come up as a result of stepping out in this way?

———————

HOW DO I GROW IN HEARING GOD'S VOICE?

1. ASK

2. SPEND TIME

3. VOCABULARY

4. RECALL

5. PAY ATTENTION

6. PAUSE

7. PROCESS

8. COMPARISON

9. TRAINING

10. BE OBEDIENT

SOME BASIC RULES FOR SHARING PROPHECY

» ALL ABOUT LOVE

» "NO DATES, NO MATES, NO DIRECTION, NO CORRECTION!"

No dates =

No mates =

No direction =

No correction =

» *NEVER* SAY, "THUS SAITH THE LORD!"

» DON'T BECOME THE PROPHECY ENFORCER

» BE ENCOURAGING! (1 Corinthians 14:3)

» BE HUMBLE

» WELCOME ACCOUNTABILITY

» RELAX, BREATHE, AND TAKE YOUR TIME!

———————————

"If I have the gift of prophecy and can fathom all mysteries and all knowledge,
and if I have a faith that can move mountains, but do not have love, I am nothing."

1 Corinthians 13:2

ACTIVATION EXERCISE

Ask God this question:

What did you sense?

How did you sense it? Did you see, hear, 'just know', or something else?

Do you have any reflections from this exercise?

INTERPRETATION

There's been a revelation. Now we need to work out if it's the Lord speaking, and if so what it means.

DIFFERENCES BETWEEN OT AND NT PROPHECY

"Today because we have the Holy Spirit, the emphasis is less on the prophet to be perfectly accurate and far more upon the process of weighing what an individual senses might be from the Lord."

"Do not quench the Spirit. Do not treat prophecies with contempt but test them all; hold on to what is good, reject every kind of evil." (1 Thessalonians 5:19-22)

The key is discernment.

SOME OF THE WAYS WE WEIGH, TEST, AND JUDGE

1. SCRIPTURE — Does it line up with the Bible?

2. LOVE — *"Follow the way of love, and eagerly desire the gifts of the Spirit, especially that you might prophesy."* (1 Cor 14:1)

3. SPEAKER — What fruit is being borne in the speaker's life?

4. WISDOM — Do other wise people think it's from God?

5. RESONANCE — "The peace of God, which transcends all understanding, will guard your hearts and your minds in Christ Jesus." (Philippians 4:7)

6. FULFILLMENT

Is it correct (if hindsight focused)?

Will it bear good fruit (if insight focused)?

Does it come true (if foresight focused)?

PROCESSING TIME

As you've listened to us teach so far, what has most impacted you? What have you found helpful — and what aren't you sure about?

Use the space below to reflect.

In your room, whether in 2s or 3s, or as a whole group, take a few minutes to share some of your responses. It's okay if not everyone is at the same place — this is how we learn from one another.

Use the space below to take notes and reflect.

APPLICATION

Some ways you can apply a prophecy:

1. PRAYER

2. ENCOURAGEMENT — *"Judas and Silas, who themselves were prophets, said much to encourage and strengthen the believers."* (Acts 15:32)

3. IDENTITY AND DESTINY — Jesus to Peter, *"On this rock I will build my church"* (Matthew 16:17-19)

4. DIRECTION — *"Now an angel of the Lord said to Philip, 'Go south to the road—the desert road—that goes down from Jerusalem to Gaza.'"* (Acts 8:26-40)

5. TEACHING — *"But the Advocate, the Holy Spirit, whom the Father will send in my name, will teach you all things and will remind you of everything I have said to you."* (John 14:26)

6. NEED FOR COUNSELING

7. EVANGELISM — *"During the night Paul had a vision of a man of Macedonia standing and begging him, 'Come over to Macedonia and help us.'"* (Acts 16:9)

8. CORRECTION — The woman at the well in John 4:17-18

9. SPIRITUAL WARFARE — *"But the prince of the Persian kingdom resisted me twenty-one days. Then Michael, one of the chief princes, came to help me, because I was detained there with the king of Persia."* (Daniel 10:13)

10. WORSHIP — Mary visits Elizabeth and worships after what God has said to her (Luke 1:39-55)

BARRIERS TO HEARING GOD

1. FALSE BELIEFS

2. FAILURE TO ASK

3. LACK OF ATTENTIVENESS

4. RATIONALISM

5. OUR AGENDA

6. SIN/ DISOBEDIENCE

7. UNFORGIVENESS

8. FEAR

9. SHAME

10. COMPARISON

11. NOISE

12. BUSYNESS

HOMEWORK

You're going to choose one practice/discipline that you're taking on in order to grow in prophecy.

For example, choose an action point from 'How to grow' or 'Rules for sharing' from the above lists.

Use the space below to record your experience.

FURTHER DISCUSSION

We encourage you as a group to continue to process this content, along with other questions that you might have.

To help the conversation, here are a few stimulus questions:

1. Look at the list of how to grow in hearing God's voice. What is one thing you can take from that list to help you grow?

2. Have you ever had someone share a prophetic word with you in a way that wasn't helpful? How could they have done it better?

3. How would you share a word if you got one?

4. How would you describe the difference between Old and New Testament prophecy?

5. How do you assess if (or how much of) a prophecy is from the Lord or not?

6. Think of a prophetic word that you have given or received. Looking at the list of applications, which of those best applied in that situation (it might be several of them)?

MODULE A2:

Healing the Sick

SESSION 1:
HOW TO MINISTER HEALING

HOMEWORK REVIEW

How did it go with your practice/ discipline in order to grow in prophecy?

Do you need to do anything else at this time to step further into prophecy?

HEALING IS A CENTRAL TASK

Healing is a major part of Jesus' activity.

"If every one of them were written down, I suppose that even the whole world would not have room for the books that would be written." (John 21:25)

"When evening came, many who were demon-possessed were brought to him, and he drove out the spirits with a word and healed all the sick. This was to fulfill what was spoken through the prophet Isaiah: 'He took up our infirmities and bore our diseases.'" (Matthew 8:16-17)

Jesus expects the same from His followers.

"Jesus gave the disciples power and authority to drive out all demons and to cure diseases and he sent them out to proclaim the Kingdom of God and to heal the sick." (Luke 9:1-2)

"They went out and preached that people should repent. They drove out many demons and anointed many sick people with oil and healed them." (Mark 6:12-13)

"He said to them, 'Go into all the world and preach the gospel to all creation. Whoever believes and is baptized will be saved, but whoever does not believe will be condemned. And these signs will accompany those who believe: In my name they will drive out demons; they will speak in new tongues; they will pick up snakes with their hands; and when they drink deadly poison, it will not hurt them at all; they will place their hands on sick people, and they will get well.'" (Mark 16:15-18)

Paul summarizes what he does:

"My message and my preaching were not with wise and persuasive words, but with a demonstration of the Spirit's power, so that your faith might not rest on human wisdom, but on God's power." (1 Corinthians 2:4)

JESUS HEALED.

HIS FIRST DISCIPLES HEALED.

THE EARLY CHURCH HEALED THE SICK.

AND — MOST RELEVANTLY — JESUS COMMANDS US TO HEAL.

SIMPLICITY

Healing the sick is so simple that small children can do it!

SELF-ASSESSMENT

How bold are you when it comes to praying for healing? Give yourself a simple rating from '1' to '5', where 5 = you do it very regularly.

Circle your answer.

1   2   3   4   5

THINK: "What will it take for you to raise your score by '1'?"

Use the space below to reflect.

WHY DID JESUS HEAL?

Jesus came to definitively reveal the nature of the Father to us.

> *"Very truly I tell you, the Son can do nothing by himself; he can do only what he sees his Father doing, because whatever the Father does the Son also does."* (John 5:19)

For Jesus, healing was a core part of His message and His ministry.

This is how Jesus wants His ministry to be assessed. *"At that very time Jesus cured many who had diseases, sicknesses and evil spirits, and gave sight to many who were blind. So he replied to the messengers, 'Go back and report to John what you have seen and heard: The blind receive sight, the lame walk, those who have leprosy are cleansed, the deaf hear, the dead are raised, and the good news is proclaimed to the poor'."* (Luke 7:21-22)

In order to explain healing, Jesus taught about the breaking in of the Kingdom of God - God's dynamic, active, and powerful rule — into our present day world.

> *"Your kingdom come, your will be done, on earth as it is in heaven."* (Matthew 6:10)

Jesus clearly believed that all the beautiful things we long for in heaven can start to be experienced today.

At the cross we discover that salvation impacts every aspect of our humanity.

Healings don't merely demonstrate that Jesus can save us, but rather they are in themselves salvation (our heavenly hope) breaking into the here and now.

SOME KEYS FOR MINISTERING HEALING

» THE GOAL IS LOVE

» STANDING ORDERS

» NOW AND NOT YET

» PERSISTENT EXPECTANCY

HEALING IS A WORK OF THE SPIRIT

"Gifts of healing..." (1 Corinthians 12:8)

PROCESSING TIME

As you've listened to this teaching so far, what has most impacted you? What have you found helpful - and what aren't you sure about?

Use the space below to reflect.

In your room, whether in 2s or 3s, or as a whole group, take a few minutes to share some of your responses. It's okay if not everyone is at the same place — this is how we learn from one another.

Use the space below to take notes and reflect.

WHAT CAUSES SICKNESS?

1. ACCIDENTS

2. ILLNESSES

3. SIN

"See, you are well again. Stop sinning or something worse may happen to you." (John 5:14)

4. SPIRITUAL CAUSES

"You deaf and mute spirit, I command you, come out of him and never enter him again." (Mark 9:25)

5. GENERATIONAL SICKNESS

Compare Deuteronomy 7:9 and Deuteronomy 5:9

6. EMOTIONAL WOUNDS

"What I have forgiven — if there was anything to forgive — I have forgiven in the sight of Christ for your sake, in order that Satan might not outwit us. For we are not unaware of his schemes." (2 Corinthians 2:10-11)

PRACTICAL MODEL

1. LISTEN — Identify the real issue.

   Ask what the person is seeking from the Lord. Listen to them – and the Holy Spirit.

2. DISCERN — "How should I pray?"

   What sort of situation is this? What sort of prayer/response is needed?

3. PRAY — Share the Father's heart.

   Discern the heart of the Father for this person/situation. Pray accordingly.

4. REVIEW — "What's going on?"

   Ask what is going on. Did they sense God/anything?

5. CLARIFY — How To Move Forward
   - If healed, share the testimony.
   - If there are lifestyle issues, what's the plan to make changes?
   - If there's an afflicting spirit, tell how to rebuke it in Jesus' name if it tries to return.
   - If not healed, affirm their value and encourage them to keep on seeking prayer.

REMEMBER: THE KEY THING IS TO WAIT + LISTEN!!

PRACTICAL TIPS

» Lay on hands — ask permission, and be smart about where you have to lay on hands.

» Let people know there may be times of quiet.

» Pray in pairs.

» Have tissues to hand.

» For healing, don't pray, 'If it be Your will'

HOMEWORK

Every time someone tells you they are sick, stop and offer to pray!

Record: who it was, what the issue was, and what happened.

Aim for at least 4 times in the next 2 weeks.

Record your experiences below.

1.

2.

3.

4.

FURTHER DISCUSSION

We encourage you as a group to continue to process this content, along with other questions that you might have.

To help the conversation, here are a few stimulus questions:

1. Look afresh at the list of where sickness originates. When do you think you might have seen some of these in operation?

2. In your own words, describe the essence of each part of the 5-step prayer model. What is the key thing you need to remember for each one?

3. Which step do you most need to grow in?

4. How do you stop the 5-step model becoming a set of rules that constrict, rather than a framework that guides?

5. When you pray for healing, do you have faith to pray very brief but bold command prayers? What holds you back from this approach?

6. Brainstorm ideas that will help those being prayed for relax and become more open to the Spirit.

MODULE A2:

Healing the Sick

SESSION 2:

HEALING AND FAITH

HOMEWORK REVIEW

Did you minister healing to anyone? What happened?

What insights or questions come up as a result of stepping out in this way?

REVIEW MODEL

1. LISTEN — Identify the real issue.

2. DISCERN — "How should I pray?"

3. PRAY — Share the Father's heart

4. REVIEW — "What's going on?"

5. CLARIFY — How To Move Forward

WHAT ABOUT WHEN PEOPLE AREN'T HEALED?

THEOLOGICAL RESPONSE

We need to be humble enough to recognize that, this side of heaven, there is an aspect of mystery about all this. We won't always receive the answers we desire.

1. STARTING POINT – GOD IS GOOD.

2. SICKNESS IS NOT PART OF GOD'S ETERNAL KINGDOM.

3. THE KINGDOM OF GOD IS BOTH THE NOW AND NOT YET.

4. WE ALWAYS HAVE AN ETERNAL HOPE.

PASTORAL RESPONSE

For others:

- Did they feel loved by you?
- More importantly, did they have an encounter with Jesus?
- If something good happened, point that out.
- If it's appropriate ask them to let you know if anything changes.

- Tell them to be persistent and keep coming to God for prayer.

- Tell them that you will keep praying (if that's true!).

- Remind them of God's goodness and His love, no matter what.

For yourself:

- Don't blame yourself

- Remember, our job is to love, God's job is to heal

- Don't let the enemy get in with disappointment or frustration

- Pray about it. Cry out to God. Be honest with Him!

- Surrender - yield your heart and the situation to Jesus

PROCESSING TIME

As you've listened to this teaching on the theological and pastoral responses to when people aren't healed, what has most impacted you?

What have you found helpful - and what aren't you sure about?

Use the space below to reflect.

In your room, whether in 2s or 3s, or as a whole group, take a few minutes to share some of your responses. It's okay if not everyone is at the same place — this is how we learn from one another.

Use the space below to take notes and reflect.

FAITH AND HEALING

Faith = *"To be firmly persuaded of God's power to accomplish His will and to display a confidence that is not shaken by circumstances"*

"Faith is a mystrious surge of confidence that God is about to act." (James Dunn)

Faith = a persistent expectancy

"In the morning I lay my requests before You and wait expectantly." (Psalm 5:3)

POP QUIZ QUESTION!

What are the two occasions in the Gospels when Jesus is described as being 'amazed'?

"He could not do any miracles there, except lay his hands on a few sick people and heal them. He was amazed at their lack of faith." (Mark 6:1-6)

"The centurion replied, 'Lord, I do not deserve to have you come under my roof. But just say the word, and my servant will be healed. For I myself am a man under authority, with soldiers under me. I tell this one, 'Go,' and he goes; and that one, 'Come,' and he comes. I say to my servant, 'Do this,' and he does it.' When Jesus heard this, he was amazed and said to those following him, 'Truly I tell you, I have not found anyone in Israel with such great faith.'" (Matthew 8:8-10)

WHOSE FAITH?

"Faith is the medium through which God releases his healing power." (John Wimber).

1. THE PERSON SEEKING HEALING

Blind Bartimaeus shouting loudly and persistently for his sight to be restored (Mark 10:46-52)

"If I just touch his clothes, I will be healed… Immediately her bleeding stopped and she felt in her body that she was freed from her suffering…'your faith has healed you. Go in peace…'" (Mark 5:25-34)

2. FRIENDS AND RELATIVES OF THE PERSON

"When Jesus saw their faith, he said to the man, 'Take heart, son; your sins are forgiven.'" (Matthew 9:2)

"Hearing this, Jesus said to Jairus, 'Don't be afraid; just believe, and she will be healed.'" (Luke 8:41-42, 49-56).

3. THOSE WHO PRAY FOR HEALING

"Walk by faith, not by sight" (2 Corinthians 5:7)

"Silver or gold I do not have, but what I do have I give you. In the name of Jesus Christ of Nazareth, walk." (Acts 3:6)

Jesus was filled with compassion for the crowds that He encountered, as they were *"like sheep without a shepherd."* (Matthew 9:35)

4. THE CHURCH COMMUNITY

"And he did not do many miracles there because of their lack of faith." (Matthew 13:58)

"Is anyone among you sick? Let them call the elders of the church to pray over them and anoint them with oil in the name of the Lord. And the prayer offered in faith will make the sick person well; the Lord will raise them up. If they have sinned, they will be forgiven." (James 5:14-15)

DISCUSS

When have you exercised faith in a (successful) supernatural healing?

What was the context? Were you praying or receiving prayer? What lessons did you learn?

In your room, whether in 2s or 3s, or as a whole group, take a few minutes to share some of your responses.

Use the space below to take notes and reflect.

HOW TO PRAY WHEN THE RECIPIENT DOESN'T HAVE MUCH FAITH

» God is the one who does the supernatural activity.

» Faith is having eyes to see into the invisible spiritual realm.

» Faith is something that can be caught from others.

PRACTICAL STEPS

1. START WITH COMPASSION

2. LOOK FOR THE FAITH

3. NO MEDICAL HISTORIES

4. REMOVE DOUBTERS

5. DECLARE TRUTH FIRST

6. ACTIVATE PROPHECY

HOW TO BUILD YOUR OWN FAITH FOR HEALING

» When praying for healing, don't say 'If it be your will that this person is healed.'

» A study of Jesus' healing ministry from the Gospels

» Read stories of healing from contemporary sources, or from church history.

» Hang out with people who operate more effectively in this ministry.

» Ask Jesus to grow your faith for the naturally supernatural to occur through you.

HOMEWORK

What is your next step to grow in praying for healing with consistency and effectiveness?

Who is going to hold you accountable for your plan?

FURTHER DISCUSSION

We encourage you as a group to continue to process this content, along with other questions that you might have.

To help the conversation, here are a few stimulus questions:

1. Why do you think faith is the thing that amazes Jesus? Why is faith so important to Him?

2. Give yourself a score between 1 and 5 (1 is low, 5 is high) as to how full of faith you are in general, and then specifically when it comes to healing.

Circle your answer.

1   2   3   4   5

3. How can you raise your own level of faith? How can you help raise the level of faith in others?

4. Think of a situation when you would be bold enough to step out and pray for healing. What does it look like? What would you say?

5. What would you say to the person if the healing comes? What would you say or do if the healing doesn't happen?

6. What other questions do you have about healing?

MODULE A3:

Naturally Supernatural Theology

SESSION 1:
THE NATURALLY SUPERNATURAL KINGDOM

HOMEWORK REVIEW

Did you set a next step to grow in praying for healing with consistency and effectiveness? What is it?

Who is holding you accountable for following through?

_____

The Kingdom of God = a guiding theological framework for naturally supernatural practice

Jesus' #1 teaching topic was _____

JESUS AND HIS PLACE IN THE KINGDOM

"The time has come. The Kingdom of God has come near. Repent and believe the good news." (Mark 1:15)

Jesus was called 'King' from the very beginning of His life. Thus the Magi asked, *"Where is the King of the Jews?"* (Matthew 2:2)

At the crucifixion, *"Pilate had a notice prepared and fastened to the cross. It read: JESUS OF NAZARETH, THE KING OF THE JEWS."* (John 19:19)

HOW 1ST CENTURY JEWS UNDERSTOOD THE KINGDOM OF GOD

- A political and geographical Kingdom

NEW TESTAMENT VIEW OF THE KINGDOM OF GOD

- It's a reign more than a realm - the Kingdom means God's active and dynamic rule.

- It is defined by spiritual rather than physical boundaries

NOW AND NOT YET

1. THE KINGDOM OF GOD IS ALREADY HERE — THE KINGDOM IS **NOW**

"But if it is by the Spirit of God that I drive out demons, then the kingdom of God has come upon you." (Matthew 12:28)

2. SIMULTANEOUSLY THE KINGDOM OF GOD IS STILL TO COME — THE KINGDOM IS **NOT YET**

"Your kingdom come, your will be done on earth as it is in heaven." (Matthew 6:10)

When Jesus returns, the whole world will acknowledge Him. *"At the name of Jesus every knee shall bow, in heaven and on earth and under the earth, and every tongue confess that Jesus Christ is Lord, to the glory of God the Father."* (Philippians 2:10,11)

"We live in the presence of the future." (George Eldon Ladd)

IN SUMMARY

The Kingdom of God breaks into this world through Jesus' works and words.
However, the Kingdom won't be fully present until His Second Coming.
Until then, the Holy Spirit empowers you and me to join Jesus
in extending God's kingly rule all around us today!

SELF-ASSESSMENT

On a scale of 1 to 10, where 1 = almost always 'Kingdom not yet', and 10 = almost always 'Kingdom now', how do you overall experience the rule of Jesus in your life?

Circle your answer.

| 1 | 2 | 3 | 4 | 5 |

| 6 | 7 | 8 | 9 | 10 |

———————

The 'Now' and the 'Not Yet' of the Kingdom of God means that we are in a battle...

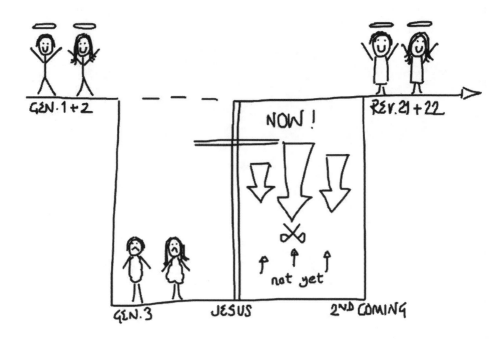

GENESIS 1 & 2

GENESIS 3 - THE FALL

JESUS COMES

JESUS' 2ND COMING

e.g. the gap from D-Day to V-E Day

THE BATTLE TODAY...

In the present day, we are between the 1st and 2nd coming of Christ.

The Kingdom of God is advancing. The realm of darkness is being driven back.

» The strong man was bound (curbing of power) so that his house can be plundered. (Matthew 12:29)

» *"And having disarmed the powers and authorities, he made a public spectacle of them, triumphing over them by the cross."* (Colossians 2:15)

» YET *"Your enemy the devil prowls around like a roaring lion looking for some-one to devour."* (1 Peter 5:8)

Remember the picket fence!

= NOW, then not yet -— NOW, then not yet — NOW, then not yet - NOW,...

- We rejoice over the wonderful things and mourn with those who don't receive now.

- We have glorious times and, sometimes almost simultaneously, great anguishes as well.

REVELATION 21 & 22

This is the most honest yet hopeful way to make sense of life.

PROCESSING TIME

What do you find most helpful in this chart?

How does it impact your understanding of the Kingdom being both now and not yet?

THE GOSPEL OF THE KINGDOM

Jesus saw the essence of His ministry as being the declaration and demonstration of the good news (or gospel) of the Kingdom.

> *"I must preach the good news of the kingdom of God to the other towns as well, because that is why I was sent."* (Luke 4:43)

- As His followers, we also must show and tell the presence of the Kingdom.

- We are not to reduce the gospel to just how we can get into heaven!

- Eternal life is defined by our relationship with God. Jesus prays, *"Now this is eternal life: that they know you, the only true God, and Jesus Christ, whom you have sent."* (John 17:3)

- The message of the Kingdom - includes forgiveness of sin, but is so much more!

THE KINGDOM AND THE CHURCH

In the New Testament, the Kingdom is not a synonym for the church.

The church consists of the people of the coming Kingdom.

We are sent to proclaim the Gospel of the Kingdom, not the Gospel of the church.

The local church gathered is an embassy of the Kingdom, which makes us Christ's ambassadors.

Our task is to bear witness to the Kingdom by our words, worship and works, carrying this to every nation and ethnicity.

DOES 'EVERYTHING HAPPEN FOR A REASON'?

Our theology must not suggest God's character is different to how it's revealed in Scripture.

» Even though God is all knowing, He chooses to self-limit Himself in this world and give freedom to His creation, so that we can build a relationship with Him. Thus His Kingdom is both now and not yet.

» The main reason terrible things happen is because we have an enemy, the devil, who seeks to poison everything. However, God is still sovereign and He offers us an eternal Kingdom perspective to even the most awful of situations.

» It is not as caring as we might think to say, "Everything happens for a reason."

- Disease, sickness, and death are works of the enemy. God does not cause them.

- Death is always an intruder into the goodness of God's creative heart.

» As disciples of Jesus we are called to join Him in driving back disease, oppression, sin, and even death itself.

HOMEWORK

Reflect on your life and identify...

» 3 areas where you tend to operate out of a 'Kingdom now' perspective

1.

2.

3.

» 3 other areas where you tend towards a 'Kingdom not yet' mentality

1.

2.

3.

These can be anything - healing, deliverance, leadership, parenting, marriage, finances, local mission, your city's governance, your kid's school, etc.

The goal of the homework is to increase your self-awareness of how you perceive the active rule of Jesus around you.

FURTHER DISCUSSION

We encourage you as a group to continue to process this content, along with other questions that you might have.

To help the conversation, here are a few stimulus questions:

1. What comes to mind when you think of the Kingdom of God?

2. How would you describe the now and not yet of the Kingdom to someone who isn't yet a Christian?

3. How do you explain the bad things that happen in life?

4. What difference will the promise of the return of Jesus make to your life this coming week?

5. Where is an area of battle in your life right now? Invite someone in the group to pray for you in that fight.

6. Who do you know who is currently facing a lot of 'Kingdom not yet'? Share what is appropriate with someone else in the group and cry out to King Jesus on their behalf.

MODULE A3:

Naturally Supernatural Theology

SESSION 2:
LIFE IN THE TENSION OF THE NOW AND THE NOT YET

HOMEWORK REVIEW

What was most encouraging from your list of ways in which you operate with a 'Kingdom now' perspective?

What was most challenging from your list of ways in which you operate with a 'Kingdom not yet' perspective?

WHY DOES 'NOT YET' OFTEN SEEM MORE REAL?

1. LIFE WITHOUT GOD

2. SPIRITUAL WARFARE, E.G. DANIEL 10:12-13

3. APATHY

4. PRIDE

5. MORE SOCIALLY ACCEPTABLE

6. RIGHTEOUS FRUSTRATION

WHAT BLOCKS THE KINGDOM NOW?

While God's power is limitless, it hits resistance (both external and internal within us) that diminishes the inbreaking of the Kingdom of God.

How to measure electrical current:

I = V / R

Current (I) = Power (V) divided by Resistance (R)

Spiritually, this translates as:

KN = HS / R

Kingdom Now (KN) = Holy Spirit Power (HS) / internal and external Resistance (R)

- What types of resistance can't you control?

- What types of resistance can you control?

- What are the points of resistance in your church culture that can be challenged?

- What are the points of resistance in your wider culture that can be challenged?

SELF-ASSESSMENT

Ask the Holy Spirit to show you the #1 area of resistance in you right now. *Remember, the Spirit will only bring conviction (= there is a pathway forward!), not condemnation (= you just feel stuck and have no hope).*

Ask the Holy Spirit to show you if there's an area of resistance in your culture (church or city) that He wants you to positively engage with.

SITTING IN THE TENSION OF THE NOW AND NOT YET

Examples from Jesus' ministry

How did He manage the tension?

HOW TO LEAN MORE INTO NOW OVER NOT YET

"What on earth could make Jesus think the kingdom was already present, when the claim was contradicted on every side? The answer lies in the presence of one element, a key characteristic of the end-time — the plenitude [abundance] of the Spirit's power. Jesus' sense of power was so overwhelming in his consciousness, so manifest in his ministry, that he could reach no other conclusion than that the end-time prophecies were already being fulfilled in his ministry, the kingdom was already present."(James Dunn)

We're not just passive victims, waiting for HS to randomly do something near us (see the man at the pool of Bethesda in John 9).

It won't be a linear, or fully predictable, process.

Sometimes the Lord makes us pursue Him for Him, rather than pursue Him for His gifts.

BECOME A LIGHTNING ROD

1. EXPECTATION

2. JOURNAL

3. OBSERVE AND LISTEN

4. ASK

5. TAKE RISKS

6. RELAX

7. TESTIMONIES

8. HUMILITY

9. PRAY IN TONGUES

10. COMMUNITY

11. DEVOUR THE GOSPELS

PROCESSING TIME

What is 1 thing you can do to become more of a lightning rod for the 'Kingdom Now' activity of the Holy Spirit?

OVERCOMING CESSATIONISM

- Some teach that there was a cessation, or ending, of the miraculous gifts of the Spirit, either with the apostles or at the completion of the Bible.

- YET there is not a single instance where the Bible even hints that the gifts of the Spirit would die out once the Bible was complete.

  "For now we see only a reflection as in a mirror; then we shall see face to face. Now I know in part; then I shall know fully, even as I am fully known."
  (1 Corinthians 13:12)

- Cessationism takes an experience - or perhaps more accurately, a lack of experience - and builds a whole theology out of it, in spite of the clear lack of Biblical support.

- Be aware that some who welcome the gifts of the Spirit have equally flawed theology and practice!

"Follow the way of love and eagerly desire gifts of the Spirit."
(1 Corinthians 14:1)

- The answer to mis-use is not no use but right use!

"If you were to lock a brand-new Christian in a room with a Bible and tell him to study what the Scriptures have to say about healing and miracles, he would never come out of the room a Cessationist." (Jack Deere)

HOMEWORK

Do you need to let go of any cessationist theology or thinking?

What are three things that you can do to lean more into the 'Now' over the 'Not yet' of the Kingdom?

1.

2.

3.

FURTHER DISCUSSION

We encourage you as a group to continue to process this content, along with other questions that you might have.

To help the conversation, here are a few stimulus questions:

1. How can you diminish resistance to the presence of God, whether in your own life or the life of the church?

2. Choose two things that will help you be more of a Holy Spirit lightning rod over the coming month. Encourage one another as people share what they will try to be doing.

3. What experience do you have of cessationism? What led you away from that path?

4. What would you say to a friend who thinks that the supernatural gifts of the Spirit are not in operation today?

5. What tips do you have for transitioning back and forth between 'rejoice with those who rejoice' and 'mourn with those who mourn'?

6. If there's someone in your group who is going through a tough time, gather round and pray for them.

Moving Forward

FURTHER READING

Over the years we have read many books on growing in the naturally supernatural. Our aim here is to give you a list that is not overwhelming, yet has a good mixture of books to help you develop in this area. We have not included books that are out of print or hard to source in the United States.

These are in author alphabetical order, and with a comment or two to introduce each book to you.

Ruth Haley Barton, *Invitation to Solitude and Silence* (2004) — One woman's journey into the necessity of regular times of withdrawing to be with Jesus. Each chapter ends with a practice or exercise to try out, which gives the book a healthy focus on application.

Mike Bickle, *Growing in the Prophetic* (1995) — From someone who pastored a church with a prominent and yet at times chaotic prophetic ministry, those lessons learned create an insightful and practical resource.

Christoph Blumhardt, *The Gospel of God's Reign* (2014) — 19th Century German theologian, also a prominent evangelist, faith healer, and politician, his writings focus on bringing God's Kingdom around us by all means possible. Stimulating, even if you don't agree with everything he says!

Shawn Bolz, *God Secrets* (2017) — Engaging teaching on developing the gift of words of knowledge, including content on what to do when you get it wrong. Shawn Bolz has a very public track record of operating in this gift, and does a good job demystifying its usage.

Michael Cassidy, *Bursting the Wineskins* (1983) — Written from an African perspective by the man who is the Honorary Chair of the Lausanne Movement, Michael uses his story as a framework to teach Biblically about entering into life in the Spirit.

Dave Clayton, *Revival Starts Here: A Short Conversation on Prayer, Fasting and Revival for Beginners Like Me* (2018) — Practical and non-guilt inducing challenge to step more into fasting and prayer, with lots of application ideas. A great short read!

Jack Deere, *Surprised by the Power of the Spirit* (1993) — The inspiring story of how a cessationist seminary professor had his life and ministry turned upside down as he experienced the power and presence of the Holy Spirit.

Don Dickerman, *When Pigs Move In* **(2009)** — A very practical book on deliverance, that contains a host of testimonies, followed by lots of details on the nuts and bolts of this vital ministry, all in an easy-to-read style.

James Dunn, *Jesus and the Spirit* **(1975)** — One of the defining scholarly works on the work of the Spirit, this is very readable and engaging. It does an excellent job of unpacking the Spirit experiences of Jesus and the Early Church. (Dunn was also Alex's NT professor at university!)

Gordon Fee, *God's Empowering Presence* **(1994)** — Fee was one of the first Pentecostals to earn a PhD in Biblical studies, and he combines the two streams in this book by literally exegeting every reference to the Spirit in Paul's writings - but the result is anything but a dry academic read.

Michael Green, *Evangelism in the Early Church* **(1970)** — A fascinating read, with all sorts of nuggets that reveal how the Early Church was so effective in reaching others with Gospel. This includes being a Spirit-filled people, and the use of the gifts is well recorded.

Bill Johnson, *God is Good* **(2016)** — An uplifting read about trusting in the goodness of God as revealed in Scripture, so that we in turn can reveal His goodness in the power of the Spirit to a broken world.

Bill Johnson & Randy Clark, *The Essential Guide to Healing* **(2011)** — An excellent book on how to heal the sick, with practical teaching, stirring stories, and sensible wisdom for developing this ministry in a church context.

Charles Kraft, *Defeating Dark Angels* **(2016)** — Clear, Biblically grounded teaching on how demonic oppression takes place, and how to minister deliverance. Kraft has many books, and we found this one to be very helpful and practical.

George Eldon Ladd, *The Gospel of the Kingdom* **(1959)** — A hugely influential book, which explores the mystery that the Kingdom of God is both now and simultaneously not yet, and how the Spirit empowers us to go out on mission to extend God's kingly rule.

George Eldon Ladd, *The Presence of the Future* **(1974)** — The big idea in this book is that the breaking in of the present, dynamic rule of God is the central concept behind Jesus' message and mission - and thus should be for ours.

Francis MacNutt, *Healing* **(1974, although look for the updated version)** — This was the first modern-era book on healing that has (deservedly) been widely read, and you can see its influence still today. Very practical and packed full of nuggets of wisdom.

Charles Price, *The Real Faith* **(1930s)** — After experiencing baptism in the Spirit in the 1920s, his ministry was transformed and saw incredible healings. This short book is the best reflection on the nature of faith and the naturally supernatural life that we have found.

Derek Prince, *They Shall Expel Demons* **(1998)** — Prince wrote numerous books on deliverance, and this is an excellent primer into this area. Sensible, Biblical, faith-filled, it contains wise teaching and helpful stories gained from many years of experience.

David Pytches, *Come Holy Spirit* **(1994)** — Written more like a logical, list-driven, logistical handbook, this was such a help in our early years of ministering in the power of the Spirit, as it gives you all the major points in a systematic way.

Jon Ruthven, *On the Cessation of the Charismata: The Protestant Polemic on Post-biblical Miracles* **(1993)** — A brilliant deconstruction of cessationism, written from a scholarly Biblical perspective, full of close exegesis of texts and clear arguments.

Jordan Seng, *Miracle Work* **(2012)** — A great overview of ministering in the spiritual gifts, with each teaching chapter followed by a short story chapter, which makes it all feel very grounded and attainable.

Sam Storms, *Practicing the Power* **(2017)** — This book does a great job of showing how stepping into the spiritual gifts is deeply rooted in Scripture. It's especially useful for those who come from a Reformed Calvinist perspective, which is the author's background.

Jerry Trousdale, *Miraculous Movements: How Hundreds of Thousands of Muslims Are Falling in Love with Jesus* **(2012)** — We both love this book! It is packed full of inspirational stories of how the church is growing globally AND gives tools that we can use here in the West.

Jerry Trousdale & Glenn Sunshine, *The Kingdom Unleashed* **(2018)** — Revealing insights on how the church in the Global South is growing rapidly through Disciple-Making Movements. Lots of takeaways on living the principles of Acts today.

Kris Vallotton, *Basic Training for the Prophetic Ministry* **(2014)** — A down-to-earth, clear and helpful training in the prophetic gifts, which feels as if a very fatherly member of your church is steering you into greater maturity!

Mark & Pam Virkler, *How to Hear God's Voice* **(2005)** — Designed more as a workbook (with lots of note taking space), it contains Biblical teaching and helpful exercises, and in particular a focus on encountering God through waiting on Him.

David & Paul Watson, *Contagious Disciple Making* **(2014)** — Learning from Disciple-Making Movements across the globe, the stories here are fabulous, and there is much content on how to make disciples in a naturally supernatural way.

Dallas Willard, *The Divine Conspiracy* **(1998)** — An engaging and thoughtful study about the nature of the Gospel of the Kingdom that Jesus preaches - which is not a set of rules to follow, but a declaration of God's active rule and His invitation for us to enter in and partner with Him.

John Wimber & Kevin Springer, *Power Evangelism* **(1985)** — Explains Jesus' theology of the Kingdom, and then moves to show how this transforms our evangelism, with lots of practical stories and ideas for taking your next step.

John Wimber & Kevin Springer, *Power Healing* **(1987)** — A classic text that has influenced many leaders. It creates a Biblical theology of healing, based on how Jesus operated, and then applies those principles with wisdom and experience.

Brother Yun, *The Heavenly Man* **(2002)** — An inspirational first-hand account from Chinese house church leader Brother Yun, who has led a huge movement in the power of the Spirit in the face of severe persecution. Some amazing stories!

NEXT STEPS

YOUR NEXT PART OF THE NATURALLY SUPERNATURAL COURSE

Congratulations on completing the Foundations part of The Naturally Supernatural Course! We hope that you have been strengthened in your awareness of the Father's love, deepened in your commitment to Jesus, and equipped to grow in a Spirit-empowered lifestyle.

The next part of The Naturally Supernatural Course is Part B: Warfare. As in this book, there are 3 modules there, covering the following topics:

Module B1: Being Filled With the Holy Spirit

- Session 1 — How to Be Filled With the Holy Spirit

- Session 2 — The Gift of Tongues

Module B2: Spiritual Warfare

- Session 1 — Biblical Ways to Understand the Battle

- Session 2 — How to Develop Wise Warfare Strategies

Module B3: How to Discern and Drive Out Demons

- Session 1 — Biblical and Practical Foundations

- Session 2 — Simple Steps to Minister Deliverance

Those are some fascinating, important, but often misunderstood (and sometimes misused) topics! You will look at them through extensive engagement with many of the relevant Scriptures, real-life stories, practical exercises, and lots of room for dialogue, processing, and personal application.

To buy access to this material, go to *naturallysupernaturalcourse.com* and follow the link to Part B: Warfare. As you've already discovered, the relevant Course Book can be purchased and shipped to you from Amazon.

ACCOMPANYING BOOKS

Over the next few years, our plan is to write a book to accompany each of the 12 modules covered in this Course. That format will allow us to include more material than is sometimes possible in these videos, while also giving a written reference guide for you to quickly access.

The first few books are already published at the time of recording the videos, with several more in the pipeline! As time goes on more will be released. You can find the books in paperback and ebook formats on Amazon.

If you would like to know whenever a new book is released, either 'follow' us as authors on Amazon (they will then email you as new books are published), or sign up for our ministry emails at *dandelionresourcing.com*.

ACCESS MORE RESOURCES

As a couple our call from God is to equip the wider church with practical tools like this book. To help facilitate this, we lead the team at Dandelion Resourcing.

As Dandelion we focus on three core areas:

- Being naturally supernatural

- Disciple-making

- Living on mission

We find that when all three of those circles of life overlap, a Kingdom culture is formed that leads to dynamic life, impact, and growth.

To help ground this into practice, and with passionate believers like you in mind, we have developed a range of resources:

FREE CONTENT

We regularly produce free short videos and articles. The focus is on our three core areas - being naturally supernatural, disciple-making, and living on mission.

If you drop your name and email in the sign-up box on dandelionresourcing.com, we'll send you an email each time a new video is released. You'll also hear about other resources and training opportunities that we develop over time. (And you can one-click unsubscribe at any time!)

NATURALLY SUPERNATURAL COACHING COHORT

The material in this Course was first taught and developed in our online small group cohorts. Aimed at Kingdom leaders, this is a 12 month process that meets as a group of 6-10 screens online twice a month.

If you are interested in finding out more, please go to *dandelionresourcing.com/ naturally-supernatural-cohort*.

BRING US TO YOUR CONFERENCE AND CHURCH

We have found that coming in person to a church or conference allows for a great depth of impact, transformation, and equipping in your local context. It's also a lot of fun to be together! Faith rises in the hearts of those who attend, by God's grace the Holy Spirit ministers, and there is a catalytic move forward.

Our heart is to resource disciples to make more disciples, so everything we do is about multiplication. Thus over a few days together, you'll likely see a whole lot of people given fresh boldness to step into the things of the Spirit. It's not about the speakers, it's about the body of Christ being equipped and empowered to go!

If you're interested in having one or both of us come in, please contact us via our ministry website, dandelionresourcing.com. While we only spend a small amount of time traveling, we do prayerfully consider every invitation.

COULD YOU HELP US OUT?

If you have enjoyed this book and course, please could you do us a quick favor?

The best way for others to find out about a resource like this is through personal recommendation (think about what makes you investigate a new book). With that in mind, we would be so honored if you would take a moment to share a quick review with others.

The #1 place is on Amazon — pop in your stars and write a comment, and that will help us enormously. (As you no doubt know, the more reviews, the more their algorithms will highlight this book - and thus the course — to others.)

In addition, please do share about this book (post a photo of you and your group holding the cover!) on social media — feel free to tag us in the shot!

Thank you so much in advance.

Again, thank you for reading — we're praying that you have so much Jesus-honoring fruitfulness as you step further into a naturally supernatural lifestyle.

With love and blessings,

Alex and Hannah

ACKNOWLEDGEMENTS

Over the years so many people have helped us grow into a naturally supernatural lifestyle. Some have been leaders, others friends, and yet others would never know our names or faces, but have shaped us through their teachings, books, podcasts, and lives.

However, a number of specific people have intentionally helped us with this book - and we are thankful for each one of them:

- Caity Shinnick designed the cover and did all the internal layout work, which turned our chicken scratch into something lovely to look at.

- Darren Galindo is our videographer, and did a wonderful job of filming and editing the accompanying videos.

- The Garden Church in Long Beach CA, who generously invested into this project and gave us space to film.

- Generous friends and donors who have supported us financially, which gives us room to write, create, plan, film, edit, and produce this material.

- Our Naturally Supernatural Coaching Cohorts, where we together worked through a lot of this material in its early forms. Your questions, stories, comments, and insights have hugely helped us hone and develop this teaching material. Obviously now any errors or mistakes in the Naturally Supernatural Course are entirely the fault of you lot and nothing to do with us!!

- Finally, to our children, we love doing this stuff with you!

ABOUT THE AUTHORS

Alex and Hannah Absalom lead Dandelion Resourcing, which empowers Christians to go and form disciple-making disciples of Jesus in naturally super-natural ways. Originally from England, they have been in church leadership since 1994, live in Long Beach CA, and with their three young adult sons are missionaries to the USA.

 dandelionresourcing.com

f facebook.com/dandelionresourcing

(O) instagram.com/alexabsalom

🐦 twitter.com/alexabsalom

Made in the USA
Columbia, SC
09 November 2022